Health and Safety
Executive

Personal protective equi

Personal Protective Equipment at Work Regulations 1992

Guidance on Regulations
L25

London: HMSO

ISBN 0 11 886334 7

Enquiries regarding this or any other HSE
publications should be made to the HSE
Information Centre at the following address:

HSE Information Centre
Broad Lane
Sheffield S3 7HQ
Tel: (0742) 892345
Fax: (0742) 892333

Contents

Introduction

1   The Personal Protective Equipment at Work Regulations came into force on 1 January 1993. The full text of the Regulations is available from HMSO. The Regulations, interspersed with respective guidance, are reproduced in Part 1 of this publication.

2   The Regulations are made under the Health and Safety at Work etc Act 1974 (HSW Act), and apply to all workers in Great Britain except the crews of sea-going ships.

3   The Regulations are based on a European Community (EC) Directive requiring similar basic laws throughout the Community on the use of personal protective equipment (PPE) in the workplace.

4   The guidance on the Regulations has been prepared by the Health and Safety Executive (HSE) for the Health and Safety Commission (HSC) after widespread consultation with industry. Part 1 deals with the main steps required under the Regulations.

5   Part 2 of this document contains advice on the selection of PPE. It considers the different types of PPE available and identifies some of the processes and activities which may require PPE to be worn. Hearing and respiratory protective equipment are not considered in this guidance as they are already dealt with by separate Regulations and guidance produced by the HSC/E.

6   Separate and more detailed guidance for specific industries is available as indicated in the text. Employers should also take into account any other HSC or HSE publications giving guidance on other Regulations, specific hazards or equipment, for example HSE booklet HS(G)53 *Respiratory protective equipment: a practical guide for users*. Up to date information on these publications can be obtained from the HSE public enquiry point.

Part 1

Guidance on the Personal Protective Equipment at Work Regulations 1992

Citation and commencement

These Regulations may be cited as the Personal Protective Equipment at Work Regulations 1992 and shall come into force on 1st January 1993.

Interpretation

-(1) In these Regulations, unless the context otherwise requires, "personal protective equipment" means all equipment (including clothing affording protection against the weather) which is intended to be worn or held by a person at work and which protects him against one or more risks to his health or safety, and any addition or accessory designed to meet that objective.

(2) Any reference in these Regulations to -

(a) a numbered regulation or Schedule is a reference to the regulation or Schedule in these Regulations so numbered; and

(b) a numbered paragraph is a reference to the paragraph so numbered in the regulation in which the reference appears.

Disapplication of these Regulations

-(1) These Regulations shall not apply to or in relation to the master or crew of a sea-going ship or to the employer of such persons in respect of the normal shipboard activities of a ship's crew under the direction of the master.

(2) Regulations 4 to 12 shall not apply in respect of personal protective equipment which is -

(a) ordinary working clothes and uniforms which do not specifically protect the health and safety of the wearer;

(b) an offensive weapon within the meaning of section 1(4) of the Prevention of Crime Act 1953 used as self-defence or as deterrent equipment;

(c) portable devices for detecting and signalling risks and nuisances;

(d) personal protective equipment used for protection while travelling on a road within the meaning (in England and Wales) of section 192(1) of the Road Traffic Act 1988, and (in Scotland) of section 151 of the Roads (Scotland) Act 1984;

(e) equipment used during the playing of competitive sports.

(3) Regulations 4 and 6 to 12 shall not apply where any of the following

Regulations apply and in respect of any risk to a person's health or safety for which any of them require the provision or use of personal protective equipment, namely -

    (a)   the Control of Lead at Work Regulations 1980;

    (b)   the Ionising Radiations Regulations 1985;

    (c)   the Control of Asbestos at Work Regulations 1987;

    (d)   the Control of Substances Hazardous to Health Regulations 1988;

    (e)   the Noise at Work Regulations 1989;

    (f)   the Construction (Head Protection) Regulations 1989.

7   Personal protective equipment (PPE) includes both the following, when they are worn for protection of health and safety:

(a)   protective clothing such as aprons, protective clothing for adverse weather conditions, gloves, safety footwear, safety helmets, high visibility waistcoats etc; and

(b)   protective equipment such as eye protectors, life-jackets, respirators, underwater breathing apparatus and safety harnesses.

8   In practice, however, these Regulations will not apply to ear protectors, most respiratory protective equipment and some other types of PPE used at work. These types of PPE are specifically excluded from the scope of the PPE at Work Regulations because they are covered by existing Regulations such as the Noise at Work Regulations 1989 (see Table 1 and paragraph 16). Even if the PPE at Work Regulations do not apply, the advice given in this guidance may still be applicable, as the general principles of selecting and maintaining suitable PPE and training employees in its use are common to all Regulations which refer to PPE.

Table 1 Provisions on the use of personal protective equipment

Where there are existing comprehensive Regulations which require PPE.	The PPE at Work Regulations will not apply.	For example: The Control of Substances Hazardous to Health Regulations 1988 require respirators to be used in certain circumstances.
Where there are no current Regulations dealing with PPE.	The PPE at Work Regulations will apply.	For example: The PPE at Work Regulations will require that chainsaw operators are provided with and wear the appropriate PPE.
Where there are existing but not comprehensive Regulations requiring the use of PPE.	The PPE at Work Regulations will apply, and will complement the requirements of the existing Regulations.	For example: regulation 19 of the Docks Regulations 1988 requires the provision of high visibility clothing when an employee is working in specific areas of a dock. The PPE at Work Regulations complement this duty by laying down duties about the accommodation of PPE, training of employees in its use etc, and may also require the use of high visibility clothing in any other part of the dock where there is a risk from vehicle movements.

9   Items such as uniforms provided for the primary purpose of presenting a corporate image, and ordinary working clothes, are not subject to these Regulations. Likewise the Regulations will not apply to 'protective clothing' provided in the food industry primarily for food hygiene purposes. However where any uniform or clothing protects against a specific risk to health and safety, for example high visibility clothing worn by emergency services, it will be subject to the Regulations. Waterproof, weatherproof or insulated clothing is subject to the Regulations if it is worn to protect employees against risks to their health or safety, but not otherwise.

10   The Regulations do not cover the use of PPE such as cycle helmets, crash helmets or motor cycle leathers worn by employees on the public highway. Motor cycle crash helmets remain legally required for motor cyclists under road traffic legislation, and Section 2 of the Health and Safety at Work etc Act 1974 (HSW Act 1974) - requiring employers to ensure the health and safety of employees, so far as is reasonably practicable - will still apply. The Regulations do apply to the use of such equipment at work elsewhere if there is a risk to health and safety, for example, farm workers riding motorcycles or 'all-terrain' vehicles should use crash helmets.

11   The Regulations do not require professional sports people to use PPE such as shin guards or head protection during competition. However, they do apply to sports equipment used in other circumstances, for example, life-jackets worn by professional canoeing instructors, riding helmets worn by stable staff, or climbing helmets worn by steeplejacks.

12   The Regulations do not require employers to provide equipment for self defence or deterrent purposes, for example personal sirens/alarms or truncheons used by security staff. However, they do apply to PPE (such as helmets or body armour) provided where staff are at risk from physical violence.

13   The Regulations do not cover personal gas detectors or radiation dosimeters. Although this equipment would come within the broad definition of PPE, the specific disapplication is included as many of the Regulations would not be appropriate to it (for example, the fitting and ergonomic requirements of regulation 4). However, employers will have a duty to provide such equipment under Section 2 of the HSW Act 1974 if its use is necessary to ensure the health and safety of employees.

Application to merchant shipping

14   Sea-going ships are subject to separate merchant shipping legislation, administered by the Department of Transport, which gives protection to people on board. Regulation 3(1) disapplies the Regulations from these ships in respect of the normal ship-board activities of a ship's crew under the direction of the master. But it does not disapply them in respect of other work activities, for example, where a shore-based contractor goes on board to carry out work on the ship, that person's activities will be subject to the Regulations within territorial waters as provided for under regulation 14. This partial exemption applies to sea-going ships only. Therefore the Regulations will apply to PPE used on ships that only operate on inland waters.

Aircraft

15   Aircraft are subject to these Regulations while on the ground and in airspace for which the United Kingdom has jurisdiction.

Application of other Regulations

16   The sets of Regulations listed in regulation 3(3) require the provision and use of certain PPE against particular hazards, and the PPE at Work Regulations will not apply where these Regulations remain in force. For example, a person working with asbestos would, where necessary, have to use respiratory protective equipment and protective clothing under the Control of Asbestos at Work Regulations 1987, rather than the PPE at Work Regulations.

17   Most older legislation on PPE has been revoked, for example the Protection of Eyes Regulations 1974; a complete list is in Schedule 3 to the Regulations. However, because they provide for the particular circumstances of the relevant industry or risk, it is necessary to retain some provisions apart from those in regulation 3(3) (for example in the Diving Operations at Work Regulations 1981 and the Docks Regulations 1988). The more comprehensive PPE at Work Regulations will apply in addition to these Regulations (see Table 1). Where necessary, therefore, employers (and others with duties under the Regulations) will have to comply with both the specific Regulations and the PPE at Work Regulations. A list of these specific Regulations is at Appendix 2.

18   Where appropriate, PPE provided by virtue of the Regulations listed in regulation 3(3) of the PPE at Work Regulations will have to comply with the requirements of the Personal Protective Equipment (EC Directive) Regulations 1992 implementing the Personal Protective Equipment Product Directive (89/686/EEC) and be 'CE' marked; as will PPE provided under these Regulations. PPE already in use can continue to be used without being 'CE' marked for as long as it remains suitable for the use to which it is being put. See paragraphs 33 to 35 for a fuller explanation.

Application to non-employees

19   These Regulations do not apply to people who are not employees, for example voluntary workers, or school children while in school. However Section 3 of the HSW Act 1974, which requires that "It shall be the duty of every employer to conduct his undertaking in such a way as to ensure, so far as is reasonably practicable, that persons not in his employment who may be affected thereby are not exposed to risks to their health and safety", will still apply. If an employer needs to provide PPE to comply with this duty, then by following the requirements of these Regulations he will fully satisfy this duty. These Regulations do apply to trainees and children on work experience programmes.

Provision of personal protective equipment

-(1) Every employer shall ensure that suitable personal protective equipment is provided to his employees who may be exposed to a risk to their health or safety while at work except where and to the extent that such risk has been adequately controlled by other means which are equally or more effective.

(2)   Every self-employed person shall ensure that he is provided with suitable personal protective equipment where he may be exposed to a risk to his health or safety while at work except where and to the extent that such risk has been adequately controlled by other means which are equally or more effective.

(3) Without prejudice to the generality of paragraphs (1) and (2), personal protective equipment shall not be suitable unless -

(a) it is appropriate for the risk or risks involved and the conditions at the place where exposure to the risk may occur;

(b) it takes account of ergonomic requirements and the state of health of the person or persons who may wear it;

(c) it is capable of fitting the wearer correctly, if necessary, after adjustments within the range for which it is designed;

(d) so far as is practicable, it is effective to prevent or adequately control the risk or risks involved without increasing overall risk;

(e) it complies with any enactment (whether in an Act or instrument) which implements in Great Britain any provision on design or manufacture with respect to health or safety in any relevant Community directive listed in Schedule 1 which is applicable to that item of personal protective equipment.

PPE as a 'last resort'

20   The Management of Health and Safety at Work Regulations (MHSWR) 1992 require employers to identify and assess the risks to health and safety present in the workplace, so enabling the most appropriate means of reducing those risks to an acceptable level to be determined. There is in effect a hierarchy of control measures, and PPE should always be regarded as the 'last resort' to protect against risks to safety and health; engineering controls and safe systems of work should always be considered first. It may be possible to do the job by another method which will not require the use of PPE or, if that is not possible, adopt other more effective safeguards: for example, fixed screens could be provided rather than individual eye protection to protect against swarf thrown off a lathe. Employers' duties in this respect are contained in much of the legislation under the HSW Act 1974, including MHSWR. The practical guidance to MHSWR given in its Approved Code of Practice is also particularly relevant. However in some circumstances PPE will still be needed to control the risk adequately, and the PPE at Work Regulations will then take effect.

21   There are a number of reasons for this approach. Firstly, PPE protects only the person wearing it, whereas measures controlling the risk at source can protect everyone at the workplace. Secondly, theoretical maximum levels of protection are seldom achieved with PPE in practice, and the actual level of protection is difficult to assess. Effective protection is only achieved by suitable PPE, correctly fitted and maintained and properly used. Thirdly, PPE may restrict the wearer to some extent by limiting mobility or visibility, or by requiring additional weight to be carried. Other means of protection should therefore be used whenever reasonably practicable.

22   Employers should, therefore, provide appropriate PPE and training in its usage to their employees wherever there is a risk to health and safety that cannot be adequately controlled by other means.

Providing personal protective equipment

23   In order to provide PPE for their employees, employers must do more than simply have the equipment on the premises. The employees must have the

equipment readily available, or at the very least have clear instructions on where they can obtain it. Most PPE is provided on a personal basis, but in certain circumstances items of PPE may be shared by employees, for example where they are only required for limited periods - see the guidance on regulation 7 (maintenance).

24   By virtue of Section 9 of the HSW Act 1974, no charge can be made to the worker for the provision of PPE which is used only at work.

25   Section 9 of the HSW Act 1974 states: "No employer shall levy or permit to be levied on any employee of his any charge in respect of anything done or provided in pursuance of any specific requirement of the relevant statutory provisions". Section 9 applies to these Regulations because they·impose a 'specific requirement' - ie, to provide PPE.

26   Regulation 4 requires PPE to be provided where risks have not been adequately controlled by other means. Where risks are sufficiently low that they can be considered in effect to be adequately controlled, then PPE need not be provided. For example, in most workplaces there will be some risk of people dropping objects onto their feet, but it is only when there is manual handling of objects of sufficient weight that the risk will be sufficient to require the provision of safety footwear.

27   Adequate control of the risk is also in general the standard of protection which the PPE provided should achieve. However there may be some circumstances where no PPE will provide adequate control of the risk (for example fire fighters' protective clothing can give only limited protection from radiant heat and flames). In these cases, the employer is required only to provide PPE offering the best protection practicable in the circumstances. Use of PPE must not increase the overall level of risk, ie PPE must not be worn if the risk caused by wearing it is greater than the risk against which it is meant to protect.

28   Regulation 4(3)(a) to (e) lists other factors which determine whether PPE is suitable. Further guidance on the suitability of PPE is given in paragraphs 29 to 35.

Ergonomic and other factors

29   When selecting PPE to be used while doing a job, the nature of the job and the demands it places on the worker should be taken into account. This will involve considering the physical effort required to do the job, the methods of work, how long the PPE needs to be worn, and requirements for visibility and communication. Those who do the job are usually best placed to know what is involved, and they should be consulted. Other factors may also influence selection: for example, PPE used in the food industry may need to be cleaned easily. The aim should always be to choose PPE which will give minimum discomfort to the wearer, as uncomfortable equipment is unlikely to be worn properly.

30   There will be considerable differences in the physical dimensions of different workers and therefore more than one type or size of PPE may be needed. The required range may not be available from a single supplier. Those having to use PPE should be consulted and involved in the selection and specification of the equipment as there is a better chance of PPE being used effectively if it is accepted by each wearer.

31   All PPE which is approved by HSE or bears the 'CE' mark must pass basic performance requirements. These have usually been set following medical advice, and the use of such PPE should cause no problems to average healthy adults. Where problems occur, employers should seek medical advice as to whether the individual can tolerate wearing the PPE. Employers are able to take into account only those medical conditions of which they have been informed.

32   In some industries, particularly those where peripatetic workers (such as contract maintenance workers or building workers) are employed, the site operator will be better placed to provide the appropriate PPE than the peripatetic worker's employer. Although under these circumstances the employer does not have to repeat the provision of suitable PPE, it is still the employer's responsibility to ensure that suitable PPE is provided. Likewise, the site operator may in practice take the action necessary to meet the requirements of the Regulations which follow, but the employer still remains responsible for ensuring that this has been done.

The quality of personal protective equipment

33   Employers must ensure that any PPE they purchase complies with the United Kingdom legislation implementing Community Directives concerning the design or manufacture of PPE with regard to health and safety, listed in Schedule 1 of the Regulations, *where that legislation is applicable*. Currently (1 January 1993) the only provision listed in Schedule 1 is the PPE Product Directive. This will be implemented by the Personal Protective Equipment (EC Directive) Regulations 1992, which will not be enforced until 1 January 1994. There are a few types of PPE such as escape equipment on aircraft that are not currently within the scope of this Directive. Regulation 4(3)(e) does not apply to this type of equipment, nor to any other type of PPE which otherwise would not have to satisfy the PPE (EC Directive) Regulations.

34   The PPE (EC Directive) Regulations require that almost all PPE supplied for use at work must be certified by an independent inspection body which will, if the PPE meets the basic safety requirements, issue a certificate of conformity. For a few types of simple PPE protecting against low risks (eg gardening gloves) the manufacturer can himself certify that the PPE meets the basic safety requirements. The manufacturer is then able to display the 'CE' mark on the product. It will be illegal for suppliers to sell PPE unless it is 'CE' marked when the PPE Product Directive is fully implemented.

35   In many cases, PPE will be made to harmonised European Standards or 'Norms' (ENs) which will systematically replace existing British Standards. These standards are published in the Official Journal of the European Communities and equipment conforming with these standards will be considered to comply with the basic safety requirements of the PPE Product Directive. Part 2 and Appendix 3 refer to some of these standards, but many ENs on PPE are still in preparation.

Compatibility of personal protective equipment

   -(1)   Every employer shall ensure that where the presence of more than one risk to health or safety makes it necessary for his employee to wear or use simultaneously more than one item of personal protective equipment, such equipment is compatible and continues to be effective against the risk or risks in question.

(2)   Every self-employed person shall ensure that where the presence of more than one risk to health or safety makes it necessary for him to wear or use simultaneously more than one item of personal protective equipment, such equipment is compatible and continues to be effective against the risk or risks in question.

36   If more than one item of PPE is being worn, the different items of PPE must be compatible with each other. For example, certain types of respirators will not fit properly and give adequate protection if a safety helmet is worn. In such cases when selecting PPE it should be ensured that both items when used together will adequately control the risks against which they are provided to protect.

Assessment of personal protective equipment

-(1)   Before choosing any personal protective equipment which by virtue of regulation 4 he is required to ensure is provided, an employer or self-employed person shall ensure that an assessment is made to determine whether the personal protective equipment he intends will be provided is suitable.

(2)   The assessment required by paragraph (1) shall include -

(a)   an assessment of any risk or risks to health or safety which have not been avoided by other means;

(b)   the definition of the characteristics which personal protective equipment must have in order to be effective against the risks referred to in sub-paragraph (a) of this paragraph, taking into account any risks which the equipment itself may create;

(c)   comparison of the characteristics of the personal protective equipment available with the characteristics referred to in sub-paragraph (b) of this paragraph.

(3)   Every employer or self-employed person who is required by paragraph (1) to ensure that any assessment is made shall ensure that any such assessment is reviewed if -

(a)   there is reason to suspect that it is no longer valid; or

(b)   there has been a significant change in the matters to which it relates,

and where as a result of any such review changes in the assessment are required, the relevant employer or self-employed person shall ensure that they are made.

Assessment

37   The purpose of the assessment provision in regulation 6 is to ensure that the employer who needs to provide PPE chooses PPE which is correct for the particular risks involved and for the circumstances of its use. It follows on from, but does not duplicate, the risk assessment requirement of the Management of Health and Safety at Work Regulations (MHSWR) 1992, which involves identifying the hazards present in any undertaking and

then evaluating the extent of the risks involved. Regulation 6(2) lays down the steps the employer should take to identify appropriate PPE.

38   Whatever PPE is chosen, it should be remembered that, although some types of equipment do provide very high levels of protection, none provides 100%. Some indication is needed of the level of risk so that the performance required of the PPE can be estimated. This information may have been gathered as part of the overall risk assessment required under MHSWR (described above), or more generalised data may be available from sources such as HSE guidance.

39   In the simplest and most obvious cases which can easily be repeated and explained at any time, the assessment to identify suitable PPE need not be recorded. In more complex cases, however, the assessment will need to be recorded and kept readily accessible to those who need to know the results.

Selection of suitable PPE

40   Once potential hazards are known there may be several types of PPE that would be suitable. The risks at the workplace and the parts of the body endangered are the two key elements to consider. A specimen risk survey table is produced as Appendix 1 and is designed to help define the areas in which workers are at risk. Part 2 identifies types of PPE that may be suitable once the risks have been assessed.

41   For example, when assessing the need for eye protection, employers should first identify the types of hazard present, such as airborne dust, liquid splashes or projectiles, and then assess the degree of risk - for example the likely size and velocity of the projectiles. They can then select a suitable type of PPE from the range of 'CE' marked equipment available. In this case, eye protection is designed for dust or chemical protection, and to different levels of impact resistance.

42   Once a type of 'CE' marked PPE has been selected for a given application, further advice and information may be necessary to ensure that the equipment can provide the protection needed. Manufacturers and suppliers have duties under the PPE (EC Directive) Regulations 1992 and under Section 6 of the Health and Safety at Work etc Act 1974 to provide information of this type.

43   When selecting PPE to be used while doing a job, the nature of the job and the demands it places on the worker should be taken into account as explained in paragraphs 29 to 32. This will involve considering the physical effort required to do the job, the methods of work, how long the PPE needs to be worn, and requirements for visibility and communication.

44   Selection should be seen as only the first stage in a continuing programme which is also concerned with the proper use and maintenance of the equipment, and the training and supervision of employees.

Maintenance and replacement of personal protective equipment

-(1) Every employer shall ensure that any personal protective equipment provided to his employees is maintained (including replaced or cleaned as appropriate) in an efficient state, in efficient working order and in good repair.

11

(2)   Every self-employed person shall ensure that any personal protective equipment provided to him is maintained (including replaced or cleaned as appropriate) in an efficient state, in efficient working order and in good repair.

45   An effective system of maintenance of PPE is essential to make sure the equipment continues to provide the degree of protection for which it was designed. Maintenance is required under the Regulations and includes, where appropriate, cleaning, disinfection, examination, replacement, repair and testing. The responsibility for carrying out maintenance should be laid down, together with the details of the procedures to be followed and their frequency. Where appropriate, records of tests and examinations should also be kept. The maintenance programme will vary with the type of equipment and the use to which it is put. For example, mechanical fall-arrestors will require a regular planned preventative maintenance programme which will include examination, testing and overhaul. However, gloves may only require periodic inspection by the user, depending on what they are being used to protect against.

46   In general, PPE should be examined to ensure that it is in good working order, before being issued to the wearer. PPE should also be examined before it is put on and should not be worn if it is found to be defective or has not been cleaned. Such examinations should be carried out by properly trained staff in accordance with the manufacturer's instructions. While most PPE will be provided on a personal basis, some may be used by a number of people. There should therefore be arrangements for cleaning and disinfecting if necessary before PPE is reissued.

47   A sufficient stock of spare parts, when appropriate, should be available to wearers. Only proper spare parts should be used in maintaining PPE, or the equipment may not provide the required degree of protection. The use of different parts may also be prohibited under regulation 4(3)(e) - some new PPE components also have to be 'CE' marked.

48   Manufacturers' maintenance schedules and instructions (including recommended replacement periods and shelf lives) should normally be followed: any significant departure from them should be discussed beforehand with the manufacturers or their authorised agent. Some British or European Standards on PPE (many of which are listed in Part 2 and in Appendix 3) also contain useful information on maintenance.

49   Simple maintenance can be carried out by the trained wearer, but more intricate repairs should only be done by specialist personnel. With complex equipment, a high standard of training will be required. As an alternative to in-house maintenance, contract maintenance services are available from both manufacturers and suppliers of equipment and specialist maintenance firms.

50   In certain circumstances it may be more appropriate, instead of instituting a specific maintenance procedure, to provide a supply of disposable PPE (eg single use coveralls) which can simply be discarded after use. If disposable PPE is used, it is important that users know when it should be discarded and replaced.

Accommodation for personal protective equipment

Where an employer or self-employed person is required, by virtue of regulation 4, to ensure personal protective equipment is provided, he shall also ensure that appropriate accommodation is provided for that personal protective equipment when it is not being used.

51   The employer needs to ensure that accommodation is provided for PPE so that it can be safely stored or kept when it is not in use. Accommodation may be simple, for example, pegs for weatherproof clothing or safety helmets. It need not be fixed, for example, safety spectacles could be kept by the user in a suitable carrying case, and PPE used by mobile workers can be stored in suitable containers in their vehicle. The storage should be adequate to protect the PPE from contamination, loss, or damage by (for example) harmful substances, damp or sunlight. Where PPE becomes contaminated during use, the accommodation should be separate from any provided for ordinary clothing (accommodation for ordinary work clothing is dealt with in the Workplace (Health, Safety and Welfare) Regulations 1992), and where necessary be suitably labelled. If the PPE itself contains hazardous materials, for example asbestos, it may need special storage arrangements.

52   Where quantities of PPE are stored, equipment which is ready for use should be clearly segregated from that which is awaiting repair or maintenance.

Information, instruction and training

-(1)   Where an employer is required to ensure that personal protective equipment is provided to an employee, the employer shall also ensure that the employee is provided with such information, instruction and training as is adequate and appropriate to enable the employee to know -

(a)   the risk or risks which the personal protective equipment will avoid or limit;

(b)   the purpose for which and the manner in which personal protective equipment is to be used; and

(c)   any action to be taken by the employee to ensure that the personal protective equipment remains in an efficient state, in efficient working order and in good repair as required by regulation 7(1).

(2)   Without prejudice to the generality of paragraph (1), the information and instruction provided by virtue of that paragraph shall not be adequate and appropriate unless it is comprehensible to the persons to whom it is provided.

53   The Regulations require employers to provide suitable information, instruction and training for their employees, to enable them to make effective use of the PPE provided to protect them against workplace hazards to their health and safety. A systematic approach to training is needed; this means that everyone who is involved in the use or maintenance of PPE should be trained appropriately.

54   Users must be trained in the proper use of PPE, how to correctly fit and wear it, and what its limitations are. Managers and supervisors must also be aware of why PPE is being used and how it is used properly. People involved in maintaining, repairing and testing the equipment and in its selection for use will also need training. Training should include elements of theory as well as practice in using the equipment, and should be carried out in accordance with the recommendations and instructions supplied by the PPE manufacturer.

55   The extent of the instruction and training will vary with the complexity and performance of the equipment. For PPE which is simple to use and maintain, safety helmets for example, some basic instructions to the users may

be all that is required. On the other hand, the safe use of anti-static footwear or laser eye protection will depend on an adequate understanding of the principles behind them, and in the case of the former, regular maintenance and testing. The instruction and training should include:

Theoretical training

(a)   an explanation of the risks present and why PPE is needed;

(b)   the operation, performance and limitations of the equipment;

(c)   instructions on the selection, use and storage of PPE related to the intended use. Written operating procedures such as permits to work involving PPE should be explained;

(d)   factors which can affect the protection provided by the PPE such as: other protective equipment; personal factors; working conditions; inadequate fitting; and defects, damage and wear;

(e)   recognising defects in PPE and arrangements for reporting loss or defects.

Practical training

(a)   practice in putting on, wearing and removing the equipment;

(b)   practice and instruction in inspection and, where appropriate, testing of the PPE before use;

(c)   practice and instruction in the maintenance which can be done by the user, such as cleaning and the replacement of certain components;

(d)   instruction in the safe storage of equipment.

Duration and frequency of training

56   The extent of the training that is required will depend on the type of equipment, how frequently it is used and the needs of the people being trained. Many manufacturers of PPE run training courses for users of their equipment and these courses may be of particular benefit to small users who do not have training facilities.

57   In addition to initial training, users of PPE and others involved with the equipment may need refresher training from time to time. Records of training details should be kept, to assist in the efficient administration of the training programme.

58   Employers must ensure not only that their employees undergo the appropriate training but that they understand what they are being taught. Employees may have difficulty in understanding their training for a number of reasons. For example, the risks (and precautions) may be of a particularly complex nature, making it difficult for employees to understand the precise nature of the protective measures they must take. English may not be the first language of some employees, and in this case the instruction and training may have to be undertaken in the employee's mother tongue to ensure comprehensibility.

Regulation 10

Use of personal protective equipment

-(1) *Every employer shall take all reasonable steps to ensure that any personal protective equipment provided to his employees by virtue of regulation 4(1) is properly used.*

(2) *Every employee shall use any personal protective equipment provided to him by virtue of these Regulations in accordance both with any training in the use of the personal protective equipment concerned which has been received by him and the instructions respecting that use which have been provided to him by virtue of regulation 9.*

(3) *Every self-employed person shall make full and proper use of any personal protective equipment provided to him by virtue of regulation 4(2).*

(4) *Every employee and self-employed person who has been provided with personal protective equipment by virtue of regulation 4 shall take all reasonable steps to ensure that it is returned to the accommodation provided for it after use.*

59   PPE should be used in accordance with the employer's instructions, which should in turn be based on the manufacturer's instructions for use. PPE should be used only after adequate training has been given to the user, and adequate levels of supervision should be provided to ensure that the training and instructions are being followed.

60   The self-employed user should ensure that he has been adequately trained to use PPE competently, to avoid creating risks to himself and others.

61   Most PPE should be returned after use to the storage place provided under regulation 8. However, there may be instances where the employee may take PPE away from the workplace, for example, some types of protective footwear or overalls. Equipment that is used or worn intermittently, welding visors for example, need only be returned at the end of the working period, shift or assignment.

Regulation 11

Reporting loss or defect

Every employee who has been provided with personal protective equipment by virtue of regulation 4(1) shall forthwith report to his employer any loss of or obvious defect in that personal protective equipment.

62   Employers should make arrangements to ensure that their employees can report to them (or their representative) the loss of or defects in PPE. These arrangements should also ensure that defective PPE is repaired or replaced before the employee concerned re-starts work.

63   Employees must take reasonable care of PPE provided and report to their employer any loss or obvious defect as soon as possible. If employees have any concerns about the serviceability of the PPE, they should immediately consult their employer or the employer's representative.

Exemption certificates

-(1) The Secretary of State for Defence may, in the interests of national security, by a certificate in writing exempt -

(a) any of the home forces, any visiting force or any headquarters from those requirements of these Regulations which impose obligations on employers; or

(b) any member of the home forces, any member of a visiting force or any member of a headquarters from the requirements imposed by regulation 10 or 11;

and any exemption such as is specified in sub-paragraph (a) or (b) of this paragraph may be granted subject to conditions and to a limit of time and may be revoked by the said Secretary of State by a further certificate in writing at any time.

(2) In this regulation -

(a) "the home forces" has the same meaning as in section 12(1) of the Visiting Forces Act 1952;

(b) "headquarters" has the same meaning as in article 3(2) of the Visiting Forces and International Headquarters (Application of Law) Order 1965;

(c) "member of a headquarters" has the same meaning as in paragraph 1(1) of the Schedule to the International Headquarters and Defence Organisations Act 1964; and

(d) "visiting force" has the same meaning as it does for the purposes of any provision of Part I of the Visiting Forces Act 1952.

Extension outside Great Britain

These Regulations shall apply to and in relation to the premises and activities outside Great Britain to which sections 1 to 59 and 80 to 82 of the Health and Safety at Work etc. Act 1974 apply by virtue of the Health and Safety at Work etc. Act 1974 (Application Outside Great Britain) Order 1989 as they apply within Great Britain.

64   The Regulations apply to all work activities carried out in British territorial waters and on offshore installations on the Continental Shelf, with the exception of those activities which are exempted by virtue of the 1989 Order and regulation 3(1). The 1989 Order identifies those work activities taking place at sea (within British jurisdiction) that will be subject to the Health and Safety at Work Act 1974.

65   These Regulations will therefore apply to those activities associated with oil and gas installation, including mobile installations, diving support vessels, heavy lift barges and pipe-lay barges.

Modifications, repeal and revocations

-*(1)   The Act and Regulations specified in Schedule 2 shall be modified to the extent specified in the corresponding Part of that Schedule.*

(2)   Section 65 of the Factories Act 1961 is repealed.

(3)   The instruments specified in column 1 of Schedule 3 are revoked to the extent specified in column 3 of that Schedule.

66   The Regulations specified in Schedule 2 have been amended to ensure that they are consistent with the requirements of the PPE at Work Regulations, particularly with regard to the assessment and provision of suitable PPE, and accommodation for PPE.

Relevant Community directive

Regulation 4(3)(e)

Council Directive of 21 December 1989 on the approximation of the laws of the Member States relating to personal protective equipment (89/686/EEC).

Modifications

Regulation 14(1)

Part I

The Factories Act 1961

1   In section 30(6), for "breathing apparatus of a type approved by the chief inspector", substitute "suitable breathing apparatus".

Part II

The Coal and Other Mines (Fire and Rescue) Order 1956

2   In Schedule 1, in regulation 23(a), for "breathing apparatus of a type approved by the Minister", substitute "suitable breathing apparatus".

3   In Schedule 1, in regulation 23(b), for "smoke helmets or other apparatus serving the same purpose, being helmets or apparatus of a type approved by the Minister,", substitute "suitable smoke helmets or other suitable apparatus serving the same purpose".

4   In Schedule 1, in regulation 24(a), for "smoke helmet or other apparatus serving the same purpose, being a helmet or other apparatus of a type approved by the Minister,", substitute "suitable smoke helmet or other suitable apparatus serving the same purpose".

Part III

The Shipbuilding and Ship-Repairing Regulations 1960

5   In each of regulations 50, 51(1) and 60(1), for "breathing apparatus of a type approved for the purpose of this Regulation", substitute "suitable breathing apparatus".

Part IV

The Coal Mines (Respirable Dust) Regulations 1975

6   In regulation 10(a), for "dust respirators of a type approved by the Executive for the purpose of this Regulation", substitute "suitable dust respirators".

Part V

The Control of Lead at Work Regulations 1980

7   In regulation 7-

(a)   after "respiratory protective equipment", insert "which complies with regulation 8A or, where the requirements of that regulation do not apply, which is"; and

(b)   after "as will", insert ", in either case,".

8   *In regulation 8, for "adequate protective clothing", substitute "protective clothing which complies with regulation 8A or, where no requirement is imposed by virtue of that regulation, is adequate".*

9   *After regulation 8, insert the following new regulations-*

"Compliance with relevant Community directives

8A   Any respiratory protective equipment or protective clothing shall comply with any enactment (whether in an Act or instrument) which implements any provision on design or manufacture with respect to health or safety in any relevant Community directive listed in Schedule 1 to the Personal Protective Equipment at Work Regulations 1992 which is applicable to that item of respiratory protective equipment or protective clothing.

Assessment of respiratory protective equipment or protective clothing

8B   -(1)   Before choosing respiratory protective equipment or protective clothing, an employer shall make an assessment to determine whether it will satisfy regulation 7 or 8, as appropriate.

(2)   The assessment required by paragraph (1) shall involve-

(a)   definition of the characteristics necessary to comply with regulation 7 or, as the case may be, 8, and

(b)   comparison of the characteristics of respiratory protective equipment or protective clothing available with the characteristics referred to in sub-paragraph (a) of this paragraph.

(3)   The assessment required by paragraph (1) shall be revised if-

(a)   there is reason to suspect that it is no longer valid; or

(b)   there has been a significant change in the work to which it relates,

and, where, as a result of the review, changes in the assessment are required, the employer shall make them. ".

10   *In regulation 9, for sub-paragraph (b), substitute the following sub-paragraph-*

"(b)   where he is required under regulations 7 or 8 to provide respiratory protective equipment or protective clothing, adequate changing facilities and adequate facilities for the storage of-

(i)   the respiratory protective equipment or protective clothing, and

(ii)   personal clothing not worn during working hours. ".

11   *At the end of regulation 13, add the following new paragraph-*

"(3) Every employee shall take all reasonable steps to ensure that any respiratory protective equipment provided to him pursuant to regulation 7 and protective clothing provided to him pursuant to regulation 8 is returned to the accommodation provided for it after use."

12   *In regulation 18(2), omit the full stop and add "and that any provision*

imposed by the European Communities in respect of the encouragement of improvements in the safety and health of workers at work will be satisfied.".

Part VI

The Ionising Radiations Regulations 1985

13   *In regulation 23(1), after "that respiratory protective equipment", insert "complies with paragraph (1A) or, where no requirement is imposed by that paragraph,".*

14   *After regulation 23(1), insert the following paragraphs-*

"(1A) For the purposes of paragraph (1), personal protective equipment complies with this paragraph if it complies with any enactment (whether in an Act or instrument) which implements in Great Britain any provision on design or manufacture with respect to health or safety in any relevant Community directive listed in Schedule 1 to the Personal Protective Equipment at Work Regulations 1992 which is applicable to that item of personal protective equipment.

(1B) Before choosing personal protective equipment, an employer shall make an assessment to determine whether it will satisfy regulation 6(3).

(1C) The assessment required by paragraph (1B) shall involve-

(a)   definition of the characteristics necessary to comply with regulation 6(3), and

(b)   comparison of the characteristics of available personal protective equipment with the characteristics referred to in sub-paragraph (a) of this paragraph.

(1D) The assessment required by paragraph (1B) shall be reviewed if-

(a)   there is reason to suspect that it is no longer valid; or

(b)   there has been a significant change in the work to which it relates,

and where, as a result of the review, changes in the assessment are required, the employer shall make them.".

15   *Add at the end of regulation 23 the following additional paragraphs-*

"(2A) Every employer shall ensure that appropriate accommodation is provided for personal protective equipment when it is not being worn.

(2B) Every employee shall take all reasonable steps to ensure that personal protective equipment provided to him is returned to the accommodation provided for it after use.".

Part VII

The Control of Asbestos at Work Regulations 1987

16   *In regulation 8(3), after "shall" the first time that word appears, insert "comply with paragraph (3A) or, where no requirement is imposed by that paragraph, shall".*

17   *Insert the following new paragraph after regulation 8(3)-*

"(3A) Any respiratory protective equipment provided in pursuance of

paragraph (2) or protective clothing provided in pursuance of regulation 11(1) shall comply with this paragraph if it complies with any enactment (whether in an Act or instrument) which implements in Great Britain any provision on design or manufacture with respect to health or safety in any relevant Community directive listed in Schedule 1 to the Personal Protective Equipment at Work Regulations 1992 which is applicable to that item of respiratory protective equipment or protective clothing.".

18   In regulation 20(2), omit the fullstop and add "and that any provision imposed by the European Communities in respect of the encouragement of improvements in the safety and health of workers at work will be satisfied.".

Part VIII

The Control of Substances Hazardous to Health Regulations 1988

19   In regulation 7, after paragraph (3), insert the following new paragraph-

"(3A) Any personal protective equipment provided by an employer in pursuance of this regulation shall comply with any enactment (whether in an Act or instrument) which implements in Great Britain any provision on design or manufacture with respect to health or safety in any relevant Community directive listed in Schedule 1 to the Personal Protective Equipment at Work Regulations 1992 which is applicable to that item of personal protective equipment.".

20   In regulation 7, in paragraph (6)(b), insert at the beginning "complies with paragraph (3A) or, where no requirement is imposed by virtue of that paragraph,".

21   In regulation 8(2), after "these regulations", insert "and shall take all reasonable steps to ensure it is returned after use to any accommodation provided for it".

Part IX

The Noise at Work Regulations 1989

22   Add the following new paragraph at the end of regulation 8-

"(3) Any personal ear protectors provided by virtue of this regulation shall comply with any enactment (whether in an Act or instrument) which implements in Great Britain any provision on design or manufacture with respect to health or safety in any relevant Community directive listed in Schedule 1 to the Personal Protective Equipment at Work Regulations 1992 which is applicable to those ear protectors.".

Part X

The Construction (Head Protection) Regulations 1989

23   Add the following paragraphs at the end of regulation 3-

"(3) Any head protection provided by virtue of this regulation shall comply with any enactment (whether in an Act or instrument) which implements any provision on design or manufacture with respect to health or safety in any relevant Community directive listed in Schedule 1 to the Personal Protective Equipment at Work Regulations 1992 which is applicable to that head protection.

(4)   Before choosing head protection, an employer or self-employed person shall make an assessment to determine whether it is suitable.

21

(5) The assessment required by paragraph (4) of this regulation shall involve-

(a) the definition of the characteristics which head protection must have in order to be suitable;

(b) comparison of the characteristics of the protection available with the characteristics referred to in sub-paragraph (a) of this paragraph.

(6) The assessment required by paragraph (4) shall be reviewed if-

(a) there is reason to suspect that it is no longer valid; or

(b) there has been a significant change in the work to which it relates,

and where as a result of the review changes in the assessment are required, the relevant employer or self-employed person shall make them.

(7) Every employer and every self-employed person shall ensure that appropriate accommodation is available for head protection provided by virtue of these Regulations when it is not being used. ".

24   For regulation 6(4), substitute the following paragraph-

"(4) Every employee or self-employed person who is required to wear suitable head protection by or under these Regulations shall-

(a) make full and proper use of it; and

(b) take all reasonable steps to return it to the accommodation provided for it after use. ".

25   In regulation 9(2), omit the full stop and add "and that any provision imposed by the European Communities in respect of the encouragement of improvements in the safety and health of workers at work will be satisfied. ".

Revocations

Regulation 14(3)

(1) Title	(2) Reference	(3) Extent of Revocation
Regulations dated 26th February 1906 in respect of the processes of spinning and weaving of flax and tow and the processes incidental thereto (the Flax and Tow-Spinning and Weaving Regulations 1906).	SR & O 1906/177, amended by SI 1988/1657.	In regulation 9, the words "unless waterproof skirts, and bibs of suitable material, are provided by the occupier and worn by the workers". Regulation 13.
Order dated 5th October 1917 (the Tin or Terne Plates Manufacture Welfare Order 1917).	SR & O 1917/1035.	Paragraph 1.
Order dated 15th August 1919 (the Fruit Preserving Welfare Order 1919).	SR & O 1919/1136, amended by SI 1988/1657.	Paragraph 1.
Order dated 23rd April 1920 (the Laundries Welfare Order 1920).	SR & O 1920/654.	Paragraph 1.
Order dated 28th July 1920 (the Gut-Scrapping, Tripe Dressing, etc. Welfare Order 1920).	SR & O 1920/1437.	Paragraph 1.
Order dated 3rd March 1921 (the Glass Bevelling Welfare Order 1921).	SR & O 1921/288.	Paragraph 1.
The Aerated Water Regulations 1921.	SR & O 1921/1932; amended by SI 1981/686	The whole Regulations.
The Sacks (Cleaning and Repairing) Welfare Order 1927.	SR & O 1927/860.	Paragraph 1.
The Oil Cake Welfare Order 1929.	SR & O 1929/534.	Paragraph 1.
The Cement Works Welfare Order 1930.	SR & O 1930/94.	Paragraph 1.
The Tanning Welfare Order 1930.	SR & O 1930/312.	Paragraph 1 and the Schedule.

(1) Title	(2) Reference	(3) Extent of Revocation
The Magnesium (Grinding of Castings and Other Articles) Special Regulations 1946.	SR & O 1946/2107.	Regulation 12.
The Clay Works (Welfare) Special Regulations 1948.	SI 1948/1547.	Regulation 5.
The Iron and Steel Foundries Regulations 1953.	SI 1953/1464; amended by SI 1974/1681 and SI 1981/1332.	Regulation 8.
The Shipbuilding and Ship-Repairing Regulations 1960.	SI 1960/1932; amended by SI 1974/1681.	Regulations 73 and 74.
The Non-Ferrous Metals (Melting and Founding) Regulations 1962.	SI 1962/1667; amended by SI 1974/1681.	Regulation 13.
The Abstract of Special Regulations (Aerated Water) Order 1963.	SI 1963/2058.	The whole Order.
The Construction (Health and Welfare) Regulations 1966.	SI 1966/95; to which there are amendments not relevant to these regulations.	Regulation 15.
The Foundries (Protective Footwear and Gaiters) Regulations 1971.	SI 1971/476.	The whole Regulations.
The Protection of Eyes Regulations 1974.	SI 1974/1681; amended by SI 1975/303.	The whole Regulations.
The Aerated Water Regulations (Metrication) Regulations 1981.	SI 1981/686.	The whole Regulations.

Part 2

Selection, use and maintenance of personal protective equipment

67   This part aims to help employers to comply with their duties to select suitable PPE and maintain it. It contains information about the main types of PPE which are widely used in industry, but does not cover more specialised and less frequently used items (for example, safety harnesses). More detailed information about particular items of PPE can be obtained from suppliers. It is also wise to involve those who will wear the PPE in its selection. Where possible, more than one model satisfying the appropriate safety performance and other criteria of suitability should be made available.

Head protection

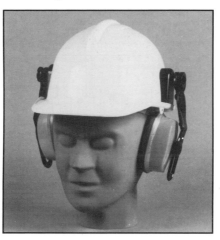 

Figure 1 Safety helmet with hearing protection   **Figure 2** Climbing helmet

Types of protection

68   There are four widely used types of head protection:

(a)   crash helmets, cycling helmets, riding helmets and climbing helmets which are intended to protect the user in falls;

(b)   industrial safety helmets which can protect against falling objects or impact with fixed objects;

(c)   industrial scalp protectors (bump caps) which can protect against striking fixed obstacles, scalping or entanglement; and

(d)   caps, hairnets etc which can protect against scalping/entanglement.

69   The following guidance deals only with industrial safety helmets, scalp protectors and climbing helmets (ie it excludes caps and hairnets).

Processes and activities

70   The following are examples of activities and processes involving risks of falling objects or impacts, which may require the provision of head protection; it is not an exhaustive list. Some of these activities will also be subject to the Construction (Head Protection) Regulations 1989:

(a)   Building work, particularly work on, underneath or in the vicinity of scaffolding and elevated workplaces, erection and stripping of formwork, assembly and installation work, work on scaffolding and demolition work.

(b)   Construction work on bridges, buildings, masts, towers, hydraulic structures, blast furnaces, steel works and rolling mills, large containers, pipelines and other large plants, boiler plants and power stations.

(c)   Work in pits, trenches, shafts and tunnels. Underground workings, quarries, opencast mining, minerals preparation and stocking.

(d)   Work with bolt-driving tools.

(e)   Blasting work.

(f)   Work near hoists, lifting plant, cranes and conveyors.

(g)   Work with blast furnaces, direct reduction plants, steelworks, rolling mills, metalworks, forging, drop forging and casting.

(h)   Work with industrial furnaces, containers, machinery, silos, storage bunkers and pipelines.

(i)   Building or repairing ships and offshore platforms.

(j)   Railway shunting work, and other transport activities involving a risk of falling material.

(k)   Slaughterhouses.

(l)   Tree-felling and tree surgery.

(m)   Work from suspended access systems, bosun's chairs etc.

71   Some relevant British and European standards:

BS 5240 Part I:1987 *Industrial safety helmets - specification for construction and performance* (To be replaced by BS EN 397)

BS 4033:1966 (1978) *Specification for industrial scalp protectors (light duty)* (To be replaced by BS EN 812)

BS 3864:1989 *Specification for protective helmets for firefighters* (To be replaced by BS EN 443)

Note: Many British Standards will be replaced by harmonised European Standards, for example BS 3864:1989 will be replaced by the European Standard EN 443. When the European Standard is introduced it will be pre-fixed by 'BS' so EN 443 will become BS EN 443 in the United Kingdom. Those with the prefix 'pr' are provisional at the time of going to print. See Appendix 3 for a more comprehensive list of appropriate standards.

The selection of suitable head protection

72   To fit, head protection should:

(a)   be of an appropriate shell size for the wearer; and

(b)   have an easily adjustable headband, nape and chin strap.

The range of size adjustment should be large enough to accommodate thermal liners used in cold weather.

73   Head protection should be as comfortable as possible. Comfort is improved by the following:

(a) a flexible headband of adequate width and contoured both vertically and horizontally to fit the forehead;

(b) an absorbent, easily cleanable or replaceable sweat-band;

(c) textile cradle straps;

(d) chin straps (when fitted) which:

    (i) do not cross the ears,

    (ii) are compatible with any other PPE needed,

    (iii) are fitted with smooth, quick-release buckles which do not dig into the skin,

    (iv) are made from non-irritant materials,

    (v) can be stowed on the helmet when not in use.

Compatibility with the work to be done

74   Whenever possible, the head protection should not hinder the work being done. For example, an industrial safety helmet with little or no peak is useful for a surveyor taking measurements using a theodolite or to allow unrestricted upward vision for a scaffold erector. If a job involves work in windy conditions, especially at heights, or repeated bending or constantly looking upwards, a secure retention system is required. Flexible headbands and Y-shaped chin straps can help to secure the helmet. Head protection worn in the food industry may need to be easily cleaned or compatible with other hygiene requirements.

75   If other PPE such as ear defenders or eye protectors are required, the design must allow them to be worn safely and in comfort. Check manufacturer's instructions regarding the compatibility of head protection with other types of PPE.

Maintenance

76   Head protection must be maintained in good condition. It should:

(a) be stored, when not in use, in a safe place, for example, on a peg or in a cupboard. It should not be stored in direct sunlight or in excessively hot, humid conditions;

(b) be visually inspected regularly for signs of damage or deterioration;

(c) have defective harness components replaced (if the design or make allows this). Harnesses from one design or make of helmet cannot normally be interchanged with those from another;

(d) have the sweat-band regularly cleaned or replaced.

77   Before head protection is reissued to another person, it should be inspected to ensure it is serviceable and thoroughly cleaned in accordance with the manufacturer's instructions, eg using soap and water. The sweat-band should always be cleaned or replaced.

Damage to shell

78   Damage to the shell of a helmet can occur when:

(a) objects fall onto it;

(b) it strikes against a fixed object;

(c) it is dropped or thrown.

Deterioration in shock absorption or penetration resistance

79   Deterioration in shock absorption or penetration resistance of the shell can occur from:

(a) exposure to certain chemical agents;

(b) exposure to heat or sunlight;

(c) ageing due to heat, humidity, sunlight and rain.

80   Chemical agents which should be avoided include paint, adhesives or chemical cleaning agents. Where names or other markings need to be applied using adhesives, advice on how to do this safely should be sought from the helmet manufacturer.

81   Exposure to heat or sunlight can make the shell go brittle. Head protection should never be stored therefore near a window, eg the rear window of a motor vehicle, because excessive heat may build up.

Replacement

82   The head protection should normally be replaced at intervals recommended by the manufacturer. It will also need replacing when the harness is damaged and cannot be replaced, or when the shell is damaged or it is suspected that its shock absorption or penetration resistance has deteriorated - for example when:

(a) the shell has received a severe impact;

(b) deep scratches occur;

(c) the shell has any cracks visible to the naked eye.

Eye protection

Figure 3   Safety goggles

Figure 4   Face shield

Types of eye protection

83   Eye protection serves to guard against the hazards of impact, splashes from chemicals or molten metal, liquid droplets (chemical mists and sprays), dust, gases, welding arcs, non-ionising radiation and the light from lasers. Eye

protectors include safety spectacles, eyeshields, goggles, welding filters, face-shields and hoods. Safety spectacles can be fitted with prescription lenses if required. Some types of eye protection can be worn over ordinary spectacles if necessary.

Processes and activities

84   The following are examples of activities and processes involving a risk to the face and eyes for which eye protectors should be used. It is not an exhaustive list.

(a)   handling or coming into contact with acids, alkalis and corrosive or irritant substances;

(b)   working with power-driven tools where chippings are likely to fly or abrasive materials be propelled;

(c)   working with molten metal or other molten substances;

(d)   during any welding operations where intense light or other optical radiation is emitted at levels liable to cause risk of injury;

(e)   working on any process using instruments that produce light amplification or radiation; and

(f)   using any gas or vapour under pressure.

Eye protectors must be provided both for persons directly involved in the work and also for others not directly involved or employed but who may come into contact with the process and be at risk from the hazards.

85   Some relevant British and European Standards:

BS 6967:1988 *Glossary of terms for personal eye protection* (To be replaced by BS EN 165)

BS 2092:1987 *Specification for eye protectors for industrial and non-industrial uses* (To be replaced by BS EN 166, 167 and 168)

BS 7028:1988 *Guide for selection, use and maintenance of eye-protection for industrial and other uses*

BS 1542:1982 *Specification for equipment for eye, face and neck protection against non-ionising radiation arising during welding and similar operations*

Note: Many British Standards will be replaced by harmonised European Standards, for example BS 3864:1989 will be replaced by the European Standard EN 443. When the European Standard is introduced it will be pre-fixed by 'BS' so EN 443 will become BS EN 443 in the United Kingdom. Those with the prefix 'pr' are provisional at the time of going to print. See Appendix 3 for a more comprehensive list of appropriate standards.

Selecting suitable eye protection

86   The selection of eye protection depends primarily on the hazard. However, comfort, style and durability should also be considered.

(a)   **Safety spectacles** are similar in appearance to prescription spectacles but may incorporate optional sideshields to give lateral protection to the eyes. To protect against impact, the lenses are made from tough optical quality plastic such as polycarbonate. Safety spectacles are generally light in weight and are available in several styles with either plastic or metal frames. Most manufacturers offer a range of prescription safety spectacles which are individually matched to the wearer.

(b) **Eyeshields** are like safety spectacles but are heavier and designed with a frameless one-piece moulded lens. Vision correction is not possible as the lenses cannot be interchanged. Some eyeshields may be worn over prescription spectacles.

(c) **Safety goggles** are heavier and less convenient to use than spectacles or eyeshields. They are made with a flexible plastic frame and one-piece lens and have an elastic headband. They afford the eyes total protection from all angles as the whole periphery of the goggle is in contact with the face. Goggles may have toughened glass lenses or have wide vision plastic lenses. The lenses are usually replaceable. Safety goggles are more prone to misting than spectacles. Double glazed goggles or those treated with an anti-mist coating may be more effective where misting is a problem. Where strenuous work is done in hot conditions, 'direct ventilation' goggles may be more suitable. However these are unsuitable for protection against chemicals, gases and dust. 'Indirect ventilation' goggles are not perforated, but are fitted with baffled ventilators to prevent liquids and dust from entering. Indirect ventilation goggles will not protect against gas or vapour.

(d) **Faceshields** are heavier and bulkier than other types of eye protector but are comfortable if fitted with an adjustable head harness. Faceshields protect the face but do not fully enclose the eyes and therefore do not protect against dusts, mist or gases. Visors on browguards or helmets are replaceable. They may be worn over standard prescription spectacles and are generally not prone to misting. Face shields with reflective metal screens permit good visibility while effectively deflecting heat and are useful in blast and open-hearth furnaces and other work involving radiant heat.

Maintenance

87   The lenses of eye protectors must be kept clean as dirty lenses restrict vision, which can cause eye fatigue and lead to accidents. There are two methods for cleaning eye protectors. Glass, polycarbonate and other plastic lenses can be cleaned by thoroughly wetting both sides of the lenses and drying them with a wet strength absorbent paper. Anti-static and anti-fog lens cleaning fluids may be used, daily if necessary, if static or misting is a problem. Alternatively lenses can be 'dry' cleaned by removing grit with a brush and using a silicone treated non-woven cloth. However plastic or polycarbonate lenses should not be 'dry' cleaned as the cloth used in this method can scratch them.

88   Eye protectors should be issued on a personal basis and used only by the person they are issued to. If eye protectors are re-issued they should be thoroughly cleaned and disinfected. Eye protectors should be protected by being placed in suitable cases when not in use. Eye protector headbands should be replaced when worn out or damaged.

89   Lenses that are scratched or pitted must be replaced as they may impair vision and their resistance to impact may be impaired. Transparent face shields must be replaced when warped, scratched or have become brittle with age.

Foot protection

Figure 5 Foundry boots

Figure 6 Insulated safety boots

Types of safety footwear

90   The following are examples of types of safety footwear:

(a)   **The safety boot or shoe** is the most common type of safety footwear.
These normally have steel toe-caps. They may also have other safety
features including slip resistant soles, steel midsoles and insulation against
extremes of heat and cold.

(b)   **Clogs** may also be used as safety footwear. They are traditionally made
from beech wood which provides a good insulation against heat and
absorbs shock. Clogs may be fitted with steel toe-caps and thin rubber
soles for quieter tread and protection against slippage or chemicals.

(c)   **Foundry boots** have steel toe-caps, are heat resistant and designed to
keep out molten metal. They are without external features such as laces to
avoid trapping molten metal blobs and should have velcro fasteners or
elasticated sides for quick release.

(d)   **Wellington boots** protect against water and wet conditions and can be
useful in jobs where the footwear needs to be washed and disinfected for
hygienic reasons, such as in the food industry. They are usually made
from rubber but are available in polyurethane and PVC which are both
warmer and have greater chemical resistance. Wellington boots can be
obtained with corrosion resistant steel toe-caps, rot-proof insoles, steel
midsoles, ankle bone padding and cotton linings. They range from ankle
boots to chest-high waders.

(e)   **Anti-static footwear** prevents the build up of static electricity on the
wearer. It reduces the danger of igniting a flammable atmosphere and
gives some protection against electric shock.

(f)   **Conductive footwear** also prevents the build up of static electricity.
It is particularly suitable for handling sensitive components or
substances (eg explosive detonators). It gives no protection against
electric shock.

Processes and activities

91   The following are examples of activities and processes involving risks to
the feet. It is not an exhaustive list.

(a) **Construction:** Work on building and demolition sites will usually require safety footwear to protect the feet against a variety of hazards, particularly objects falling on them, or sharp objects (eg nails) on the ground piercing the shoe and injuring the sole of the foot.

(b) **Mechanical and manual handling:** There may be a risk of objects falling on or crushing the front of the foot. There may be a risk of a fall through slipping which could result in damage to the heel on impact. There is also a danger of treading on pointed or sharp objects which can penetrate the shoe and injure the sole of the foot

(c) **Electrical:** People who work where there are flammable atmospheres should wear anti-static footwear to help prevent ignitions due to static electricity. Such footwear is similar to conventional footwear in that the soles are sufficiently insulated to give some measure of protection against electric shock.

(d) **Thermal:** Working in cold conditions requires footwear with thermal insulation. Work in hot conditions requires footwear with heat-resistant and insulating soles.

(e) **Chemical:** Footwear provided when working with hazardous chemicals should be both impermeable and resistant to attack by chemicals.

(f) **Forestry:** Forestry chain-saw boots are water-resistant and are designed to offer protection against chain-saw contact.

(g) **Molten substances:** Foundry boots that are easily removed should be provided where there is a danger of splashing by molten substances.

92 Some relevant British and European Standards:

BS 1870:Part 1:1988 *Specification for safety footwear other than all rubber and all plastic moulded compounds*

BS 1870:Part 2:1986 *Specification for lined rubber safety boots*

BS 1870:Part 3:1981 *Specification for PVC moulded safety footwear*

BS 4676:1983 *Specification for gaiters and footwear for protection against burns and impact risks in foundries*

BS 4972:1973 *Specification for women's protective footwear*

BS 5145:1989 *Specification for lined industrial vulcanised rubber boots*

BS 5462: *Footwear with midsole protection:*

BS 5462:Part 1:1984 *Specification for lined vulcanised rubber footwear with penetration resistant midsoles*

BS 5462:Part 2:1984 *Specification for lined or unlined polyvinyl chloride (PVC) footwear with penetration resistant midsoles*

BS 6159: *Polyvinyl chloride boots:*

BS 6159:Part 1:1987 *Specification for general and industrial lined or unlined boots*

Note: Many British Standards will be replaced by harmonised European Standards, for example BS 3864:1989 will be replaced by the European Standard EN 443. When the European Standard is introduced it will be pre-fixed by 'BS' so EN 443 will become BS EN 443 in the United Kingdom. Those with the prefix 'pr' are provisional at the time of going to print. See Appendix 3 for a more comprehensive list of appropriate standards.

Selecting suitable foot protection

93   The selection of foot protection depends primarily on the hazard. However, comfort, style and durability should also be considered. The choice should be made on the basis of suitability for protection, compatibility with the work and the requirements of the user.

94   Generally, safety footwear should be flexible, wet resistant and absorb perspiration. Inflexible or unnecessarily bulky footwear will result in tired feet and legs. Boots and not shoes are required where ankles need protection. You should consider the ability of the footwear to resist corrosion, abrasion and industrial wear and tear. Always follow the manufacturer's instructions and markings for appropriate use and level of protection.

(a)   **Soles**: Work shoes and boots should have treaded soles for slip-resistance. Soles can be heat and oil resistant, slip resistant, shock resistant, anti-static or conductive. Footwear intended to protect against oils, solvents or liquids need soles that are moulded or bonded to the upper. Soles that are stitched or glued may separate and expose the foot to hazard. Footwear with steel midsoles should be used where there is a risk that the sole could be pierced by nails and similar objects.

(b)   **Steel toe-caps:** They should be capable of resisting a heavy sharp object falling from a considerable height. Footwear complying with BS 4676 will offer this resistance.

(c)   **Heat resistance:** Leather or other heat resistant materials can be used in safety footwear to offer protection against heat, sparks and molten metal.

(d)   **Waterproofing:** People working in wet places should wear safety footwear impervious to water. Rubber and PVC are suitable inexpensive water-proofing materials for footwear but they are not permeable. There are 'breathable materials' which are water resistant, but which also allow air to get through and perspiration to get out, and may therefore be more comfortable and more hygienic. However, footwear manufactured from this type of material tends to be more expensive.

95   Electrical hazards: The following provide protection against electrical hazards.

(a)   **Anti-static footwear:** Anti-static footwear offers suitable protection against the hazard of static electricity and will give some protection against mains electric shock. Anti-static footwear must be worn where there is both a hazard from static build up and the possibility of contact with mains electricity. The soles must have a resistance low enough to allow static electricity to leak slowly away while maintaining enough resistance to protect against a 240 volt mains electricity shock.

(b)   **Conductive footwear** offers greater protection against static electricity and is used where the wearer handles very sensitive components or materials. *It must not be worn where there is a danger of electric shock.* The soles of conductive footwear must have an electrical resistance low enough to enable static electricity to be taken quickly away from the body to the earth.

96   Leg protection: The following are examples of leg protection.

(a)   People working around molten metal need protection for their lower legs. For example this can be achieved by the use of foundry boots and gaiters, or a high foundry boot worn inside molten metal protective trousers.

(b)   Hard fibre or metal guards should be used to protect shins against impact. The top of the foot up to the ankle can be protected by added-on metatarsal guards.

Maintenance

97   Safety footwear should be maintained in good condition, checked regularly and discarded if worn or deteriorated. Laces should be checked and replaced if necessary. Materials lodged into the tread should be removed. The stitching should be checked for loose, worn or cut seams. Spraying the upper layers of new footwear with a silicone spray or applying a protective wax will give extra protection against wet conditions.

Hand and arm protection

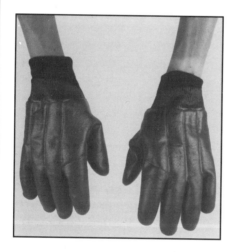
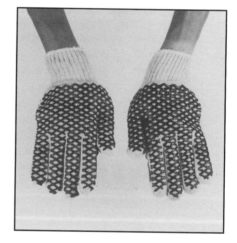

Figure 7 Vinyl-coated insulated gloves   **Figure 8** General purpose work gloves

Types of hand protection

98   Gloves of various designs provide protection against a range of industrial hazards, including:

(a)   cuts and abrasions;

(b)   extremes of temperature, hot and cold;

(c)   skin irritation and dermatitis;

(d)   contact with toxic or corrosive liquids.

99   The type and degree of protection depends on the glove material and the way in which it is constructed. Barrier creams may sometimes be used as an aid to skin hygiene in situations where gloves cannot be used. Experience shows, however, that barrier creams are less reliable than suitable gloves as a means of chemical protection.

Processes and activities

100 The following processes and activities involve risk of injury to the hands or hazards for which hand protection may be necessary. It is not an exhaustive list.

(a) **Manual handling:** Hands may be pierced by abrasive, sharp or pointed objects or damaged by impact when handling goods. However, gloves should not be worn when working near moving equipment and machinery parts as the glove may get caught in the equipment and draw the hand and arm of the worker into the moving machinery.

(b) **Vibration:** Gloves are essential to keep hands warm in cold weather when operating machines that cause vibrations such as pneumatic drills and chain-saws. Vibration White Finger occurs more frequently and more severely when the hands and fingers are cold as the blood supply to the fingers is reduced by the body in an attempt to conserve heat.

(c) **Construction and outdoor work:** Keeping the hands warm and supple in cold weather is important when working on a building site handling scaffolding, bricks and timber. Manual dexterity is lost when the hands are cold, which can lead to accidents if articles are dropped. Gloves protect against hazards in site clearance such as previous contamination of soil which may contain disease spores that may seriously infect small cuts and abrasions.

(d) **Hot and cold materials:** Gloves will also protect against hazards from handling hot or cold materials and work involving contact with naked flames or welding.

(e) **Electricity:** Danger from electric shock.

(f) **Chemical:** There are many tasks where the hands may come into contact with toxic or corrosive substances. Examples include maintenance of machinery, cleaning up chemical spillages and mixing and dispensing pesticide formulations. If correctly selected and used, gloves provide a barrier between the wearer's skin and the harmful substance, preventing local damage, or in some cases absorption through the skin.

(g) **Radioactivity:** Danger from contamination when handling radio-active materials

101 Some relevant British and European Standards:

BS 1651:1986 *Specification for industrial gloves*

BS 697:1986 *Specification for rubber gloves for electrical purposes*

Note: Many British Standards will be replaced by harmonised European Standards, for example BS 3864:1989 will be replaced by the European Standard EN 443. When the European Standard is introduced it will be pre-fixed by 'BS' so EN 443 will become BS EN 443 in the United Kingdom. Those with the prefix 'pr' are provisional at the time of going to print. See Appendix 3 for a more comprehensive list of appropriate standards.

Selecting suitable hand protection

102 Gloves or other hand protection should be capable of giving protection from hazards, be comfortable and fit the wearer. The choice should be made on the basis of suitability for protection, compatibility with the work and the requirements of the user. You should consider the ability of protective gloves

to resist abrasion and other industrial wear and tear. Always follow the manufacturer's instructions and markings for appropriate use and level of protection. When selecting gloves for chemical protection, reference should be made to chemical permeation and resistance data provided by manufacturers.

(a) **Penetration and abrasion:** Gloves made from chain-mail or leather protect against penetration and abrasion. Gloves made from knitted Kevlar will provide protection against cuts and gloves manufactured from Kevlar needlefelt give good puncture resistance.

(b) **Thermal protection:** Depending upon their weight and construction, terrycloth gloves will provide protection against heat and cold. Gloves made from neoprene are good for handling oils in low temperatures. Gloves manufactured from other materials such as Kevlar, glass fibre and leather can be used to provide protection at higher temperatures.

(c) **Fire resistance:** Chromed leather gloves are fire retardant.

(d) **Chemicals protection:** Chemical protective gloves are available in a range of materials including natural rubber, neoprene, nitrile, butyl, PVA, PVC and viton. The degree of protection against chemical permeation depends on the glove material, its thickness and method of construction. As a general rule, gloves for use in handling toxic liquids should be chosen on the basis of breakthrough time. This means that the duration of use should not exceed the breakthrough time quoted by the manufacturer of the glove for the chemical substance concerned. Laboratory testing may be required in order to establish adequacy in some applications. When handling dry powders, any chemically resistant glove may be used. The durability of the gloves in the workplace should also be considered. Some glove materials may be adversely affected by abrasion.

(e) **General use gloves:** Rubber, plastic or knit fabric gloves are flexible, resist cuts and abrasions, repel liquids and offer a good grip. Rubber gloves allow a sensitive touch and give a firm grip in water or wet conditions. Leather, cotton knit or other general purpose gloves are suitable for most other jobs. General use gloves should only be used to protect against minimal risks to health and safety (eg for gardening and washing up and similar low risk tasks).

Maintenance

103 Care should be taken in the donning, use, removal and storage of protective gloves. They should be maintained in good condition, checked regularly and discarded if worn or deteriorated. Gloves should be free of holes or cuts and foreign materials and their shape should not be distorted. They should fit the wearer properly leaving no gap between the glove and the wearer's sleeve.

104 Gloves should always be cleaned according to the manufacturer's instructions as they may have particular finishes which may make the following general guidance inappropriate. For example, repeated washing may remove fungal and bacterial inhibitors from the lining of the glove which may ultimately lead to skin irritation. And there is also the risk of cross contamination as chemical residues can remain on the gloves even after washing.

105 Contact between the gloves and chemicals should be kept to a minimum as some chemicals can alter the physical characteristics of a glove and impair its protective properties. Gloves contaminated by chemicals should be washed as

soon as possible and before their removal from the hands. Grossly contaminated gloves should be discarded. Gloves contaminated on the inside can be dangerous as the chemical contamination will be absorbed by the skin. Wear armlets if there is a danger of chemicals entering the glove at the cuff.

106   When wearing protective gloves do not touch other exposed parts of the body, equipment or furniture as contamination can be transferred to them. Cotton liners can be worn if hands sweat profusely.

Care for the hands when handling chemicals

107   Do not let chemicals come into contact with the skin. Wash hands frequently, dry them carefully and use a hand cream to keep the skin from becoming dry through loss of natural oils. Keep cuts and abrasions covered with waterproof plasters and change the dressing for a porous one after work. Handle and remove gloves carefully to avoid contamination of hands and the insides of the gloves.

Protective clothing for the body

Figure 9   High visibility coat   **Figure 10**   Lamex apron

Types of protection

108   Types of clothing used for body protection include:

(a)   coveralls, overalls and aprons to protect against chemicals and other hazardous substances;

(b)   outfits to protect against cold, heat and bad weather;

(c)   clothing to protect against machinery such as chain-saws.

109   Types of clothing worn on the body to protect the person include:

(a)   high visibility clothing;

(b)   life-jackets and buoyancy aids.

Processes and activities

110   The following are examples of the sorts of processes and activities that require protective clothing for the body. It is not an exhaustive list.

37

(a)   Laboratory work or work with chemicals, dust or other hazardous substances;

(b)   construction and outdoor work;

(c)   work in cold-stores;

(d)   forestry work using chainsaws;

(e)   highway and road works;

(f)   work on inland and inshore waters;

(g)   spraying pesticides;

(h)   food processing;

(i)   welding;

(j)   foundry work and molten metal processes;

(k)   fire-fighting.

111   Some relevant British and European Standards:

BS 1771:Part I:1989 *Specification for fabrics of wool and wool blends*

BS 1771:Part 2:1984 *Specification for fabrics of cellulosic fibres, synthetic fibres and blends*

BS 1547:1959 *Specification for flameproof industrial clothing (materials and design)*

BS 6249:1982 *Materials and material assemblies used in clothing for protection against heat and flame*

BS 6249:Part 1:1982 *Specification for flammability testing and performance*

BS 3791:1970 *Specification for clothing for protection against intense heat for short periods*

BS 2653:1955 *Specification for protective clothing for welders*

BS 5426:1987 *Specification for workwear and career wear*

BS 3595: 1981 *Specification for life-jackets*

Note: Many British Standards will be replaced by harmonised European Standards, for example BS 3864:1989 will be replaced by the European Standard EN 443. When the European Standard is introduced it will be pre-fixed by 'BS' so EN 443 will become BS EN 443 in the United Kingdom. Those with the prefix 'pr' are provisional at the time of going to print. See Appendix 3 for a more comprehensive list of appropriate standards.

Selection

112   Protection from chemicals and hazardous substances:

(a)   **Low risk chemicals** can be protected against by wearing chemical-resistant clothing, coveralls and laboratory coats made from uncoated cotton or synthetic material such as nylon or Terylene with a water repellant finish.

(b) **Strong solvents, oils and greases** require heavier protection afforded by coats, overalls and aprons made from neoprene or polyurethane coated nylon, or Terylene or rubber aprons.

(c) **Chemical suits** protect against more potent chemicals. They are totally encapsulating suits which are either vapour-proof or liquid-splash proof and are fed with breathable air. They must be washed in warm water and a mild soap whenever they have come into contact with chemicals. The suit should be hung up to dry before being stored in cases or hung on hangers. Chemical suits have a life expectancy of three to four years and should be inspected every three months even if not in use. This entails an air test and looking at all of the seams.

(d) **Vapour suits** protect against hazardous vapours and are made of butyl, polyvinyl chloride (PVC), viton, a combination of viton and butyl or teflon. They should be air-tested with the manufacturer's test kit, before being stored in a protective case. Manufacturers of vapour proof suits generally provide a testing and repair service consisting of a visual inspection and air test.

(e) **Splash-resistant suits** are also made from the same polymers but may also be made of limited-use bonded olefin fabrics.

(f) **Fibres and dust:** Protection can be obtained by wearing suits made from bonded olefin that forms a dense shield which keeps out fibres and particles.

113 Thermal and weather protection:

(a) **Keeping dry:** Jackets, trousers and leggings made with PVC coated nylon or cotton will offer protection against rain. These materials are also resistant to abrasions, cracking and tearing and will protect against most oils, chemicals and acids. 'Breathable' water-proof fabrics will keep out water while allowing body perspiration to escape. Waxed cotton will also protect against rain.

(b) **Keeping warm:** Minus 25 and Minus 50 suits are available which are guaranteed to protect at these respective sub zero temperatures. More limited protection can be obtained from quilted and insulated coats and vests.

(c) **Keeping cool:**

  (i) Aluminium-asbestos clothing made of dust-suppressed materials is heat-resistant. The outside is made of aluminium and the inside lining is cotton. This type of clothing is suitable for hot work, for example in foundries.

  (ii) Welding and foundry clothing is flame retardant and is mainly of flame retardant cotton or wool materials. Chrome leather is used for aprons etc.

  (iii) Molten metal splash clothing is heat resistant and should resist molten metal splash up to 1600 degrees centigrade.

  (iv) Cotton or cotton and polyester coveralls with flame-retardant finishes are available to protect against sparks and flame.

114 Food processing: Food quality overalls and coveralls will protect against splashes from oils and fats. Butchers and slaughterhouse workers should wear lamex or chain-mail aprons if there is a risk of injury to the abdomen or chest, for example when using knives or choppers.

115 Chainsaw protective clothing: The front of the leg is most vulnerable to chainsaw accidents although the back of the leg is also at risk. Protective legwear incorporates layers of loosely woven long synthetic fibres. On contact with the saw chain, the fibres are drawn out and clog the chain saw sprocket, causing the chain to stop. Legwear is available with all-round protection or with protection only for the front of the legs. The legwear with all round protection offers the greatest protection for users. Jackets and gloves are also available with inserts of chainsaw resistant materials at vulnerable points. See paragraph 91(f) in the section on chainsaw boots.

Personal protection worn on the body

High visibility clothing

116 This is made from PVC impregnated with fluorescent pigments. This should be worn by workers on roadsides and other areas where it is important to be seen to be safe. BS 6629 sets out three grades of high visibility clothing:

(a) Class A refers to coats and jackets offering the highest degree of conspicuousness.

(b) Class B refers to waistcoats and tabards and offers a lower level of conspicuousness.

(c) Appendix G is concerned with exposure to a particular risk such as that faced by road workers.

117 Chapter 8 of the Department of Transport Traffic Signs Manual requires all personnel on or near carriageways wear high visibility garments complying with BS 6629 'Class A or B to Appendix G or better'. The Department of Transport also recommends that Class A with sleeves to Appendix G is used on motorways and other high speed roads.

Personal buoyancy equipment

118 Life-jackets or buoyancy aids should be worn where there is a foreseeable risk of drowning when working on or near water.

(a) **A life-jacket** is a personal safety device which, when fully inflated (if inflatable), will provide sufficient buoyancy to turn and support even an unconscious person face upwards within five seconds (ten seconds if automatically inflated). The person's head will be supported with the mouth and nose well clear of the water.

Some people are reluctant to wear life-jackets as they find them bulky and restrictive. However, either an automatically inflatable life-jacket or a type which is inflated by a manual pull-cord should overcome these problems. These are usually compact and allow for a full range of movement.

(b) **Buoyancy aids** are worn to provide extra buoyancy to assist a conscious person in keeping afloat. However, they will not turn over an unconscious person from a face down position.

Maintenance

119 Protective clothing should only be used for the purpose intended. It should be maintained in good condition and checked regularly. It should be repaired or discarded if damaged.

Specimen risk survey table for the use of personal protective equipment

Risks

The PPE at Work Regulations 1992 apply except where the Construction (Head Protection) Regulations 1989 apply — covering the Mechanical and Thermal risks.

The CLW, IRR, CAW, COSHH and NAW Regulations[1] will each apply to the appropriate hazard.

PARTS OF THE BODY		Falls from a height	Blows, cuts, impact, crushing	Stabs, cuts, grazes	Vibration	Slipping, falling over	Scalds, heat, fire	Cold	Immersion	Non-ionising radiation	Electrical	Noise	Ionising radiation	Dust fibre	Fume	Vapours	Splashes, spurts	Gases, vapours	Harmful bacteria	Harmful viruses	Fungi	Non-micro biological antigens
		Mechanical					Thermal															
Head	Cranium																					
Head	Ears																					
Head	Eyes																					
Head	Respiratory tract																					
Head	Face																					
Head	Whole head																					
Upper limbs	Hands																					
Upper limbs	Arms (parts)																					
Lower limbs	Foot																					
Lower limbs	Legs (parts)																					
Various	Skin																					
Various	Trunk/abdomen																					
Various	Whole body																					

(1) The Control of Lead at Work Regulations 1980, The Ionising Radiations Regulations 1985, The Control of Asbestos at Work Regulations 1987, The Control of Substances Hazardous to Health Regulations 1988, The Noise at Work Regulations 1989.

Legislation on PPE applying in addition to the Regulations

The Coal and Other Mines (Fire and Rescue) Regulations 1956 SI 1956/1768 HMSO (regulations 23-25)

The Construction (Working Places) Regulations 1966 SI 1966/94 HMSO ISBN 0 11 100264 8 (regulation 38)

The Coal Mines (Respirable Dust) Regulations 1975 SI 1975/1433 HMSO ISBN 0 11 051433 5 (regulation 10)

The Dangerous Substances in Harbour Areas Regulations 1987 SI 1987/37 HMSO ISBN 0 11 076037 6 (regulation 17(1)(b) & (2)(b))

The Diving Operations At Work Regulations 1981 SI 1981/399 HMSO ISBN 0 11 016399 0 (regulations 5(1), 7(1), 9(1), 12(1,4 & 5), 13)

The Docks Regulations 1988 SI 1988/1655 HMSO ISBN 0 11 087655 5 (regulations 2(1), 19)

The Electricity at Work Regulations 1989 SI 1989/635 HMSO ISBN 0 11 096635 X (regulations 4(4), 14)

The Offshore Installations (Operational Safety Health and Welfare) Regulations 1976 SI 1976/1019 HMSO ISBN 0 11 061019 9 (regulation 16 and Schedule 4)

The Offshore Installations (Life Saving Appliances) Regulations 1977 SI 1977/486 HMSO ISBN 0 11 070486 X (regulation 7)

Provisions dealing with entry into confined spaces

The Factories Act 1961 Chapter 34 HMSO 1961 ISBN 0 10 850027 6 (Section 30)

The Docks Regulations 1988 SI 1988/1655 HMSO ISBN 0 11 087655 5 (regulation 18)

The Ship Building and Ship Repairing Regulations 1960 SI 1960/1932 (regulations 50, 51 and 60)

The Breathing Apparatus etc (Report on Examination) Order 1961 SI 1961/1345 HMSO ISBN 0 11 100320 2 (The whole order)

British and European Standards

Head protection

BS 3864:1989 *Specification for protective helmets for firefighters* (To be replaced by BS EN 443)

BS 4033:1966 *Specification for industrial scalp protectors (light duty)* (To be replaced by BS EN 812)

BS 4423:1969 *Specification for climbers' helmets*

BS 4472:1988 *Specification for protective skull caps for jockeys*

BS 5240 Part I:1987 *Industrial safety helmets - specification for construction and performance* (To be replaced by BS EN 397)

BS 6473:1984 *Specification for protective hats for horse and pony riders*

Eye protection

BS 1542:1982 *Specification for equipment for eye, face and neck protection against non-ionising radiation arising during welding and similar operations*

BS 2092:1987 *Specification for eye protection for industrial and non-industrial uses* (To be replaced by BS EN 166, 167 and 168)

BS 6967:1988 *Glossary of terms for personal eye protection* (To be replaced by BS EN 165)

BS 7028:1988 *Guide for selection, use and maintenance of eye-protection for industrial and other uses*

BS EN 169 *Personal eye protection: Filters for welding and related techniques: Transmittance requirements and recommended use*

BS EN 170 *Personal eye protection: Ultraviolet filters: Transmittance requirements and recommended use*

BS EN 171 *Personal eye protection: Infrared filters: Transmittance requirements and recommended use*

prEN 165 *Personal eye protection: Vocabulary*

prEN 166 *Personal eye protection: Specifications*

prEN 167 *Personal eye protection: Optical test methods*

prEN 168 *Personal eye protection: Non-optical test methods*

Footwear

BS 953:1979 *Methods of test for safety and protective footwear*

BS 1870: Part 1:1988 *Specification for safety footwear other than all rubber and all plastic moulded compounds*

BS 1870: Part 2:1976 (1986) *Specification for lined rubber safety boots*

BS 1870: Part 3:1981 *Specification for polyvinyl chloride moulded safety footwear*

BS 2723:1956 (1988) *Specification for fireman's leather boots*

BS 4676:1983 *Specification for gaiters and footwear for protection against burns and impact risks in foundries*

BS 4972:1973 *Specification for women's protective footwear*

BS 5145:1989 *Specification for lined industrial vulcanised rubber boots*

BS 5462: *Footwear with midsole protection:*

BS 5462:Part I:1984 *Specification for lined vulcanised rubber footwear with penetration resistant midsoles*

BS 5462:Part 2:1984 *Specifiction for lined or unlined polyvinyl chloride (PVC) footwear with penetration resistant midsoles*

BS 6159:*Polyvinyl chloride boots:*

BS 6159:Part 1:1987 *Specification for general and industrial lined or unlined boots*

BS 7193:1989 *Specification for lined lightweight rubber overshoes and overboots*

The following will probably replace BS 1870 and BS 953:

prEN 344 *Requirements and test methods for safety protective and occupational footwear for professional use*

prEN 345 *Specification for safety footwear for professional use*

prEN 346 *Specification for protective footwear for professional use*

prEN 347 *Specification for occupational footwear for professional use*

prEN 381 *Protective clothing for users of hand held chain saws: Part 3 Test method for boots*

Gloves

BS 697:1986 *Specification for rubber gloves for electrical purposes*

BS 1651:1986 *Specification for industrial gloves*

BS EN 421 *Protective gloves against ionising radiation to include irradiation and contamination*

prEN 374 (Parts 1 to 5) *Protective gloves against chemicals and micro-organisms*

prEN 381 (Parts 1 to 6) *Protective gloves for users of hand held chain saws*

prEN 388 *Protective gloves: Mechanical test methods and specifications*

prEN 407 *Protective gloves against thermal hazards*

prEN 420 *General requirements for gloves*

prEN 511 *Protective gloves against cold*

prEN 659 *Fire-fighters' gloves: Protection against heat and flame*

Protective clothing

BS 1547:1959 *Specification for flameproof industrial clothing (materials and design)*

BS 1771:Part 1:1989 *Specification for fabrics of wool and wool blends*

BS 1771:Part 2:1984 *Specification for fabrics of cellulosic fibres, synthetic fibres and blends*

BS 2653:1955 *Specification for protective clothing for welders*

BS 3595:1981 *Specification for life-jackets*

BS 3791:1970 *Specification for clothing for protection against intense heat for short periods*

BS 5426:1987 *Specification for workwear and career wear*

BS 6249:1982 *Materials and material assemblies used in clothing for protection against heat and flame*

BS 6249:Part 1:1982 *Specification for flammability testing and performance*

BS 6629:1985 *Specification for optical performance of high visibility garments and accessories for use on the highway*

prEN 340 *General requirements for protective clothing*

prEN 342 *Protective clothing against cold weather*

prEN 343 *Protective clothing against foul weather*

prEN 366 *Protective clothing: protection against heat and fire: method of test: evaluation of materials and material assemblies when exposed to a source of radiant heat*

prEN 367 *Protective clothing: Method of determining heat transmission on exposure to flame*

prEN 373 *Protective clothing: Assessment of resistance of materials to molten metal splash*

prEN 381 (Parts 1 to 6) *Protective clothing for users of hand held chainsaws*

prEN 393 *Life-jackets and personal buoyancy aids: buoyancy aids, 50 N*

prEN 394 *Life-jackets and personal buoyancy aids: additional items*

prEN 395 *Life-jackets and personal buoyancy aids: life-jackets, 100 N*

prEN 396 *Life-jackets and personal buoyancy aids: life-jackets, 150 N*

prEN 399 *Life-jackets and personal buoyancy aids: life-jackets, 275 N*

prEN 463 *Chemical protective clothing: protection against liquid chemicals: method of test: determination of resistance to penetration by liquids (Jet Test)*

prEN 464 *Chemical protective clothing: protection against gases and vapours: method of test: determination of leak tightness (internal pressure test)* prEN 465 *Protective clothing: protection against liquid chemicals: performance requirements: type 4 equipment: protective suits with spray-tight connections between different parts of the protective suit*

prEN 466 *Chemical protection clothing: protection against liquid chemicals (including liquid aerosols): performance requirements: type 3 equipment: chemical protective clothing with liquid-tight connections between different parts of the clothing*

prEN 467 *Protective clothing: protection against liquid chemicals: performance requirements: type 5 equipment garments providing chemical protection to parts of the body*

prEN 468 *Chemical protective clothing: protection against liquid chemicals: method of test: determination of resistance to penetration by spray*

prEN 469 *Protective clothing for fire-fighters*

prEN 470 *Protective clothing for use in welding and similar activities*

prEN 471 *High visibility warning clothing*

prEN 510 *Protective clothing against the risk of being caught up in moving parts*

prEN 531 *Protective clothing for industrial workers exposed to heat (excluding fire-fighters' and welders' clothing)*

prEN 532 *Clothing for protection against heat and flame: Method of test for limited flame spread*

prEN 533 *Clothing for protection against heat and flame: Performance specification for limited flame spread of materials*

prEN 702 *Protective clothing: Protection against heat and fire - Test method: Determination of the contact heat transmission through protective clothing or its materials*

Further reading

Priced publications

Control of Lead at Work: Approved Code of Practice 2nd rev ed COP 2 HMSO 1985 ISBN 0 11 883780 X

Control of substances hazardous to health and Control of carcinogenic substances. Control of Substances Hazardous to Health Regulations 1988 Approved Code of Practice L5 4th ed HMSO 1993 ISBN 0 11 882085 0

Construction (Head Protection) Regulations 1989 Guidance on Regulations HMSO 1990 ISBN 0 11 885503 4

Health and Safety at Work etc Act Chapter 37 1974 HMSO ISBN 0 10 543774 3

Management of Health and Safety at Work Approved Code of Practice L21 HMSO 1992 ISBN 0 11 886330 4

Manual Handling Guidance on Regulations HMSO 1992 ISBN 0 11 886335 5

Noise at Work. Noise guide no 1: legal duties of employers. Noise guide no 2: legal duties of designers, manufacturers, importers and suppliers HMSO 1989 ISBN 0 11 885512 3

Personal Protective Equipment (EC Directive) Regulations 1992 (SI 1992/3139) HMSO. ISBN not available at time of going to print

Protection of persons against ionising radiation arising from any work activity: The Ionising Radiations Regulations 1985: Approved Code of Practice COP 16 HMSO 1985 ISBN 0 11 883838 5

Respiratory Protective Equipment: A practical guide for users HS(G)53 HMSO 1990 ISBN 0 11 885522 0

Safety in docks: Docks Regulations 1988: Approved Code of Practice with Regulations and Guidance COP 25 HMSO 1988 ISBN 0 11 885456 9

Work Equipment Guidance on Regulations HMSO 1992 ISBN 0 11 886332 0

Work with asbestos insulation, asbestos coating and asbestos insulating board Approved Code of Practice rev ed COP 3 1988 HMSO ISBN 0 11 883979 9

Free leaflets

HSE *Agriculture Information Sheet No 1 Personal buoyancy equipment on inland and inshore waters* 1989

HSE *A Ceramic Industry Booklet: Personal protective equipment* 1992 IAC/L56

Construction Information Sheets - dealing with personal protective equipment (To be published February 1993 and available from HSE Area Offices. See Yellow Pages for the telephone number of your local Area Office)

HSE *Protective clothing and footwear in the construction industry* 1991 IAC/L16

HSE *Safety with chainsaws* 1990 AS20

Free leaflets are available from the HSE Information Centre. Address at the front of this book.

Printed in the United Kingdom for HSE, published by HMSO